MW00958493

I Am Who I Am

By: S.R.Tease

copyright 2020 by S.R. Tease © All rights reserved.

www.purplesquirrelworld.com

I Am Who I Am

By: S.R.Tease

copyright 2020 by S.R. Tease © All rights reserved.

www.purplesquirrelworld.com

I am who I am,

and I'm proud to be black.

I was born to be me,

that's a matter of fact.

You could travel the world,

take a rocket through space,

but nothing can compare

to the smile on my face.

I am who I am.

I'm a diamond, a pearl.

I'm a handsome black boy.

I'm a pretty black girl.

I have coolness and class

in the way that I walk.

I have a musical sound

in the way that I talk.

I am who I am,

and I move to a beat,

as the rhythm of Africa

stirs in my feet.

While the joy of the continent

runs through my veins,

and the souls of my ancestors rise again.

I am who I am,

and there is nothing I'd change.

What nature has built,

I would not rearrange.

From my frizzy, black hair

to my ebony skin.

There is beauty outside,

and there is beauty within.

I am who I am.

I will listen and learn.

I will stay on the path

without taking a turn.

No there won't be a limit

to what I'll achieve,

if I work really hard

and I dare to believe.

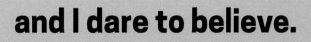

I am who I am.

I am young and I'm free.

I can be all the things

that I dream I can be.

Like a dentist, a lawyer,

a keeper of bees,

or a clown who does tricks

on the flying trapeze.

I am who I am.

I am healthy and strong.

I hold my head high,

that's where it belongs.

I am gentle and kind

and I help when I can.

I choose every day

to be part of God's plan.

I am who I am.

I am brave, I am tough.

I won't run away

when the going gets rough.

I'm determined. I'm focused.

I know that I'm smart.

I think with my brain,

and I choose with my heart.

I am who I am,

with my own point of view.

You cannot be me

and I cannot be you.

My voice is important

and deserves to be heard.

I can create change

with each powerful word.

I am who I am.

I am friendly and fun.

I laugh, I sing, I play, I run.

I'm a curious child

who loves to explore.

I have a great personality that's hard to ignore.

 I am who I am,

a future queen or a king.

I am treasured and blessed.

It's a magical thing.

Of course I'm not perfect,

but I'm perfectly me.

And that is exactly who I was meant to be.

I am who I am.

I am beautifully made.

I will create new paths.

I will invent new ways.

I am entirely unique

and to myself I'll be true.

There is no one like me and

there is no one like you!

WE ARE WHO WE ARE!

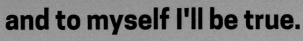

Page from "I Am Who I Am" coloring activity book.
Available on AMAZON

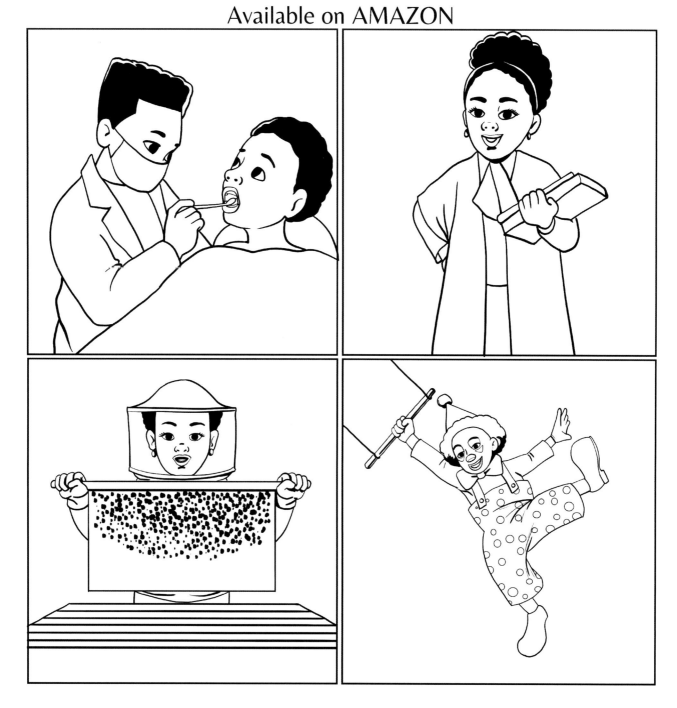

5 THINGS I LIKE ABOUT ME

1. _____

2. _____

3. _____

4. _____

5. _____

Made in the USA
Columbia, SC
06 November 2020

24069771R00015

5 THINGS I LIKE ABOUT ME

1. _____

2. _____

3. _____

4. _____

5. _____

Made in the USA
Columbia, SC
06 November 2020

24069771R00015